SCIENCE CHUNKS

Year B Student Notebook

Science Chunks - Year B Notebook

First Edition 2021

ISBN: 978-1-953490-11-7

Copyright @ Elemental Science, Inc.
Email: support@elementalscience.com

Copyright Policy

Table of Contents

Human Body Unit

Building Blocks

Cells

_____

_____

_____

_____

_____

_____

_____

_____

_____

_____

_____

DNA

_____

_____

_____

_____

_____

_____

_____

_____

_____

_____

_____

Skin and Hair

Skin

_____
_____
_____
_____
_____
_____
_____

_____
_____
_____

Hair

_____
_____
_____
_____
_____
_____
_____
_____

_____
_____
_____
_____

Skeletal System

Skeleton

_____

_____

_____

_____

_____

_____

_____

_____

Skull

_____

_____

_____

_____

_____

_____

_____

_____

Bones

_____

_____

_____

_____

_____

_____

_____

_____

Muscular System

Joints

_____
_____
_____
_____
_____
_____
_____

Muscles

_____
_____
_____
_____
_____
_____
_____

How Muscles Work

_____
_____
_____
_____
_____
_____

Nervous System

Brain

_____
_____
_____
_____
_____
_____
_____
_____

Nervous System

_____
_____
_____
_____
_____
_____
_____

Sleep

_____
_____
_____
_____
_____
_____
_____

Circulatory System
Heart

_____
_____
_____
_____
_____
_____
_____

Blood Vessels

_____
_____
_____
_____
_____
_____

Blood

_____
_____
_____
_____
_____
_____

The Five Senses

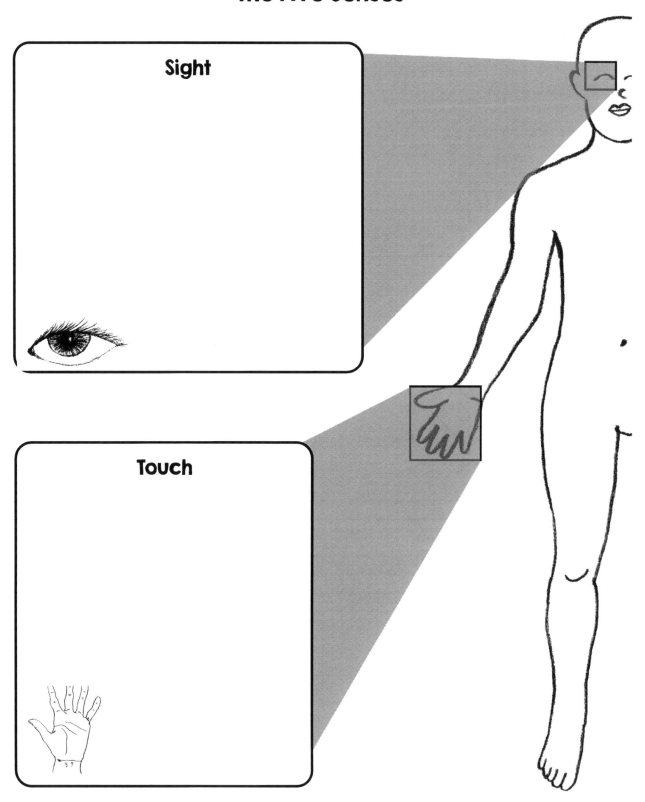

Sight

Touch

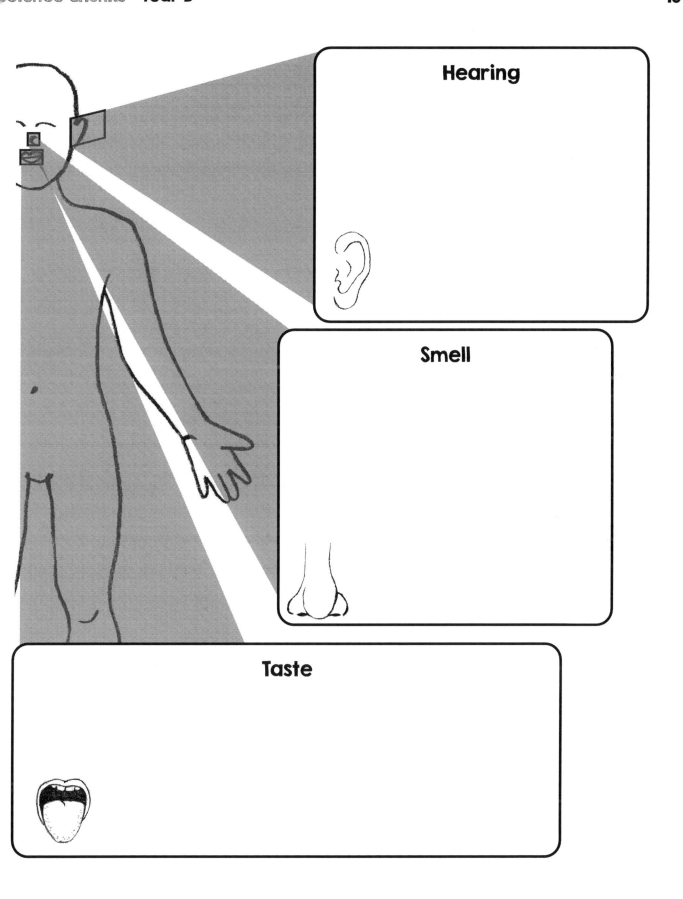

Hearing

Smell

Taste

Respiratory System

Lungs

_____
_____
_____
_____
_____
_____
_____
_____

Alveoli

_____
_____
_____
_____
_____
_____
_____

Breathing

Inhalation
(Breathing In)

_____
_____
_____
_____
_____
_____
_____

Digestive System

Digestive System

_____

_____

_____

_____

_____

_____

_____

Teeth

_____

_____

_____

_____

_____

_____

_____

Intestines

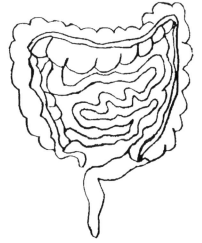

_____

_____

_____

_____

_____

_____

Urinary System
Urinary System

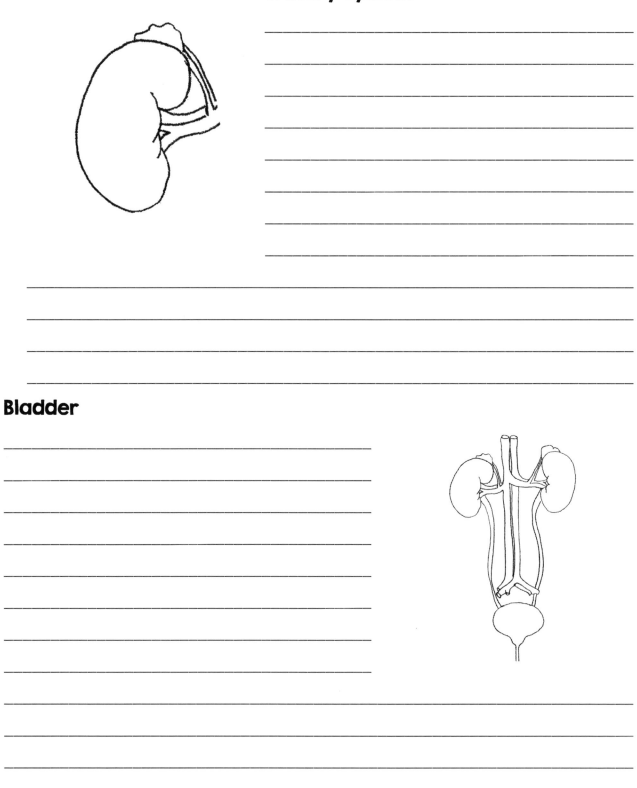

_____

_____

_____

_____

_____

_____

_____

_____

_____

_____

_____

Bladder

_____

_____

_____

_____

_____

_____

_____

_____

_____

_____

_____

_____

Immune System

Germs

_____
_____
_____
_____
_____
_____
_____
_____

Body Defenses

_____
_____
_____
_____
_____
_____
_____

Allergies

_____
_____
_____
_____
_____
_____
_____

Weather Unit

The Sun and Atmosphere

The Sun

_____

_____

_____

_____

_____

_____

_____

_____

_____

_____

Atmosphere

_____

_____

_____

_____

Exosphere

Thermosphere

Mesosphere

Layers of the Atmosphere

Stratosphere

_____

Troposphere

Sea Level

_____

_____

_____

Climate

_____
_____
_____
_____
_____
_____
_____
_____
_____
_____
_____
_____
_____
_____
_____
_____
_____
_____
_____
_____
_____
_____
_____
_____

Weather and Wind

Water Cycle and Clouds

Clouds

_____

_____

_____

_____

_____

_____

_____

_____

_____

_____

_____

The Water Cycle

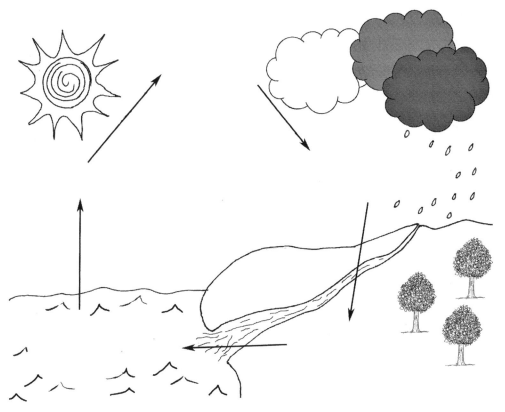

Storms and Rain

Weather Forecasting

_____

_____

_____

_____

_____

_____

_____

_____

_____

_____

_____

_____

_____

_____

_____

_____

_____

_____

_____

_____

_____

_____

_____

Stars Unit

Stars

_____
_____
_____
_____
_____
_____
_____
_____
_____
_____
_____
_____
_____
_____
_____
_____
_____
_____

- -
- -
- -
- -
- -
- -
- -

Ursa Major and Ursa Minor

Ursa Major

Ursa Minor

Winter Constellations

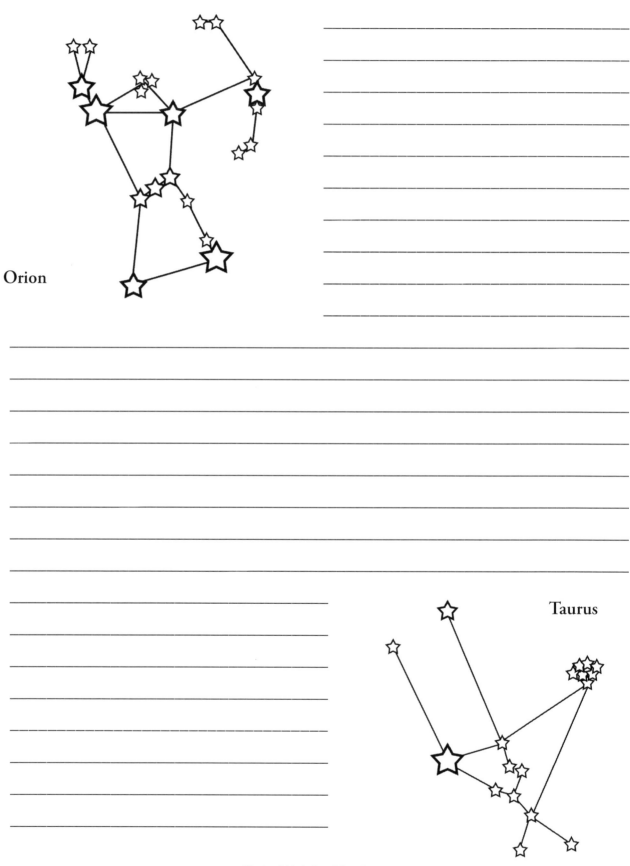

Orion

Taurus

Spring Constellations

_____

_____

_____

_____

_____

_____

_____

_____

_____

_____

_____

Leo

_____

_____

_____

_____

_____

_____

_____

_____

_____

_____

_____

_____

Virgo

Summer Constellations

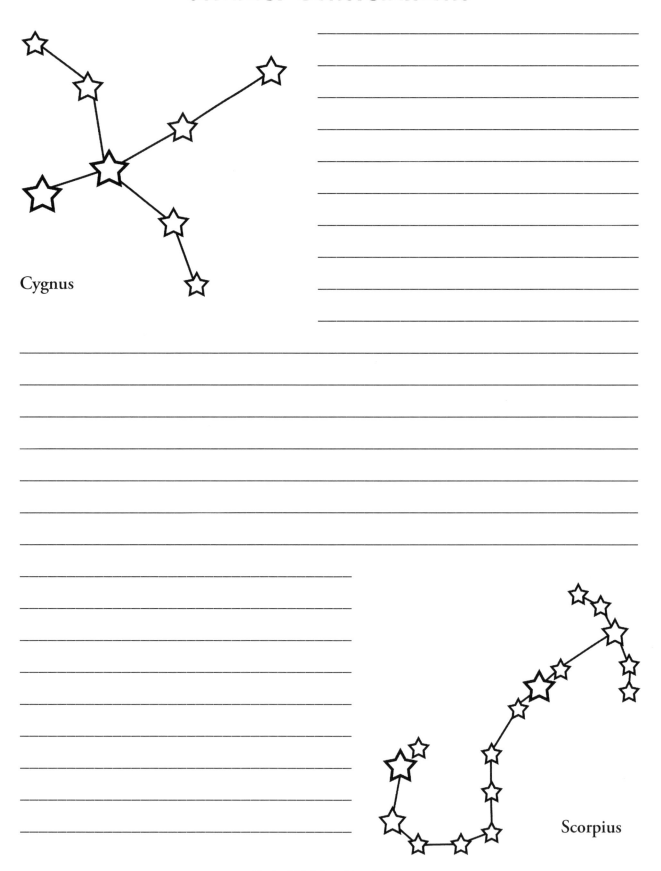

Cygnus

Scorpius

Fall Constellations

Pegasus

Andromeda

Matter Unit

States of Matter

Solid

_____
_____
_____
_____
_____
_____
_____
_____

Liquid

_____
_____
_____
_____
_____
_____
_____

Gas

_____
_____
_____
_____
_____
_____
_____

Changes in State

Melting   Freezing

_____   _____

_____   _____

_____   _____

_____   _____

Boiling   Condensing

_____   _____

_____   _____

_____   _____

_____   _____

Liquid Behavior

How Liquids Behave

_____

_____

_____

_____

_____

_____

_____

Evaporation

_____

_____

_____

_____

_____

_____

_____

Surface Tension

_____

_____

_____

_____

_____

_____

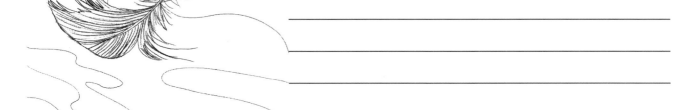

Gas Behavior

Brownian Motion

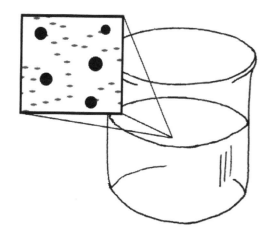

_____
_____
_____
_____
_____
_____
_____
_____

Diffusion

_____
_____
_____
_____
_____
_____

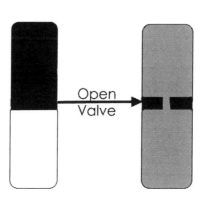

Open Valve

Pressure and Temperature

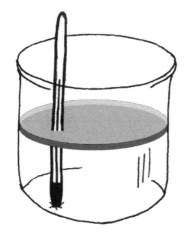

_____
_____
_____
_____
_____
_____
_____

SCIENCE CHUNKS

Acid and Bases Unit

Acids and Bases

Acids

_____
_____
_____
_____
_____
_____
_____
_____

_____
_____
_____
_____

Bases

_____
_____
_____
_____
_____
_____
_____

_____
_____
_____
_____

pH

pH

14
13
12
11
10
9
8
7 — Neutral
6
5
4
3
2
1
0

Basic Range

Acidic Range

_____

_____

_____

_____

_____

_____

_____

_____

_____

_____

_____

_____

Indicator

_____

_____

_____

_____

_____

_____

_____

Neutral

Base   Acid

_____

_____

_____

_____

Neutralization

Neutralization

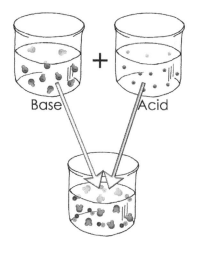

Base + Acid

_____

_____

_____

_____

_____

_____

_____

_____

_____

_____

_____

Salts

_____

_____

_____

_____

_____

_____

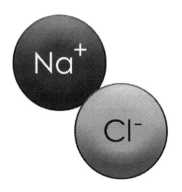

_____

_____

_____

_____

Pasteur Unit

Louis Pasteur - His Life

Louis Pasteur - His Work

Pasteur

The Founder
of Germ Theory

1800

1825

1850

1875

1900

Energy Unit

Energy

Energy

Energy Resources

Solar Energy

_____
_____
_____
_____
_____
_____
_____

Wind Energy

_____
_____
_____
_____
_____
_____
_____

Fossil Fuel

_____
_____
_____
_____
_____
_____
_____

Nuclear Energy

Nuclear Fusion

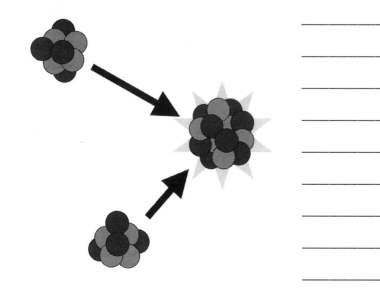

_____
_____
_____
_____
_____
_____
_____
_____
_____
_____

_____
_____
_____

Nuclear Fission

_____
_____
_____
_____
_____
_____
_____
_____
_____
_____
_____

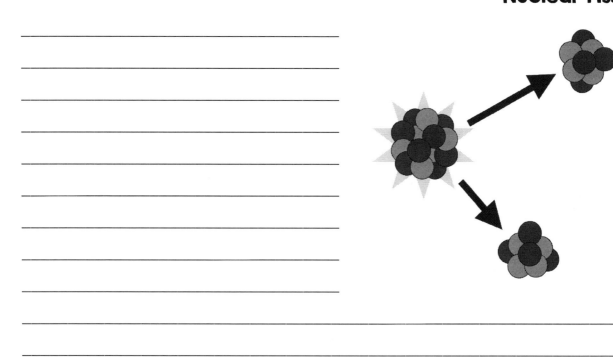

Heat Energy

Heat and Temperature

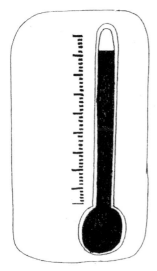

_____

_____

_____

_____

_____

_____

_____

_____

_____

_____

_____

_____

_____

_____

_____

_____

_____

_____

_____

_____

_____

_____

_____

_____

_____

Heat Transfer

Conduction

_____

_____

_____

_____

_____

_____

_____

Convection

_____

_____

_____

_____

_____

_____

Radiation

_____

_____

_____

_____

_____

_____

_____

Glossary

Year B Glossary

A

Acid —

Alveoli —

Atmosphere —

Layers of the Atmosphere

Exosphere

Thermosphere

Mesosphere

Stratosphere

Troposphere

B

Bacteria —

_____

_____

_____

_____

Base —

_____

_____

_____

_____

Blood Vessel —

_____

_____

_____

_____

C

Cells —

_____

_____

_____

_____

Climate —

Conduction —

Constellation —

Convection —

D

Diffusion —

_____

_____

_____

_____

Digestion —

_____

_____

_____

_____

E

Energy —

_____

_____

_____

_____

Energy Chain —

_____

_____

_____

_____

Evaporation —

_____

_____

_____

_____

F

Fermenation —

_____

_____

_____

_____

G

H

Heat —

_____

_____

_____

_____

I

Indicator —

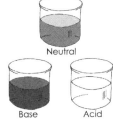

_____

_____

_____

_____

J

K

Kidney —

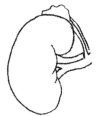

_____

_____

_____

_____

L

M

Microbes —

_____

_____

_____

_____

Muscle —

_____
_____
_____
_____

N

Natural Cycle —

_____
_____
_____
_____

Neuron —

_____
_____
_____
_____

Neutralization —

Base   +   Acid

_____
_____
_____
_____

Nuclear Fission —

_____
_____
_____
_____

Nuclear Fusion —

_____
_____
_____
_____

O

P

pH —

_____
_____
_____
_____

Physical Change —

_____
_____
_____
_____

Precipitation —

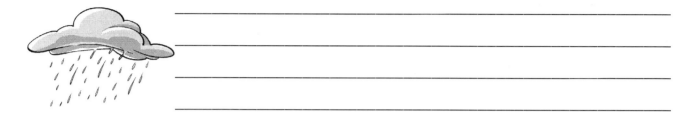

_____
_____
_____
_____

Q

R

Radiation —

_____
_____
_____
_____

S

Salt —

_____
_____
_____
_____

Senses —

The
Five
Senses

_____
_____
_____
_____

Skeleton —

_____

_____

_____

_____

Solar Energy —

_____

_____

_____

_____

Star —

_____

_____

_____

_____

States of Matter —

_____

_____

_____

_____

Sublimation —

Solid → Gas

Surface Tension —

T

Temperature —

Thunderstorm —

Tornado —

_____

_____

_____

_____

U

V

Vapor —

_____

_____

_____

_____

Volume —

_____

_____

_____

_____

W

Wind Energy —

_____
_____
_____
_____

X

Y

Yeast —

_____
_____
_____
_____

Z

Made in the USA
Columbia, SC
21 April 2022

59215720R00039